DEAN

First published in Great Britain 2020 by Farshore
This edition published 2021 by Dean, part of Farshore
An imprint of HarperCollins*Publishers*
1 London Bridge Street, London SE1 9GF
www.farshore.co.uk

HarperCollins*Publishers*
Macken House, 39/40 Mayor Street Upper,
Dublin 1, D01 C9W8, Ireland

ISBN 978 0 0085 0760 2
Printed and Bound in the UK using 100% Renewable Electricity at CPI Group (UK) Ltd
005

Written and designed by Cloud King Creative.

A CIP catalogue record for this title is available from the British Library.

This book is produced from independently certified FSC™ paper
to ensure responsible forest management.

For more information visit: www.harpercollins.co.uk/green

POKéMON
Pocket
Puzzles

™

Do you have what it takes to become a top Trainer, just like Ash and his friends?

Join Ash Ketchum and his buddy Pikachu as they explore the islands of the tropical Alola region. There are fascinating Pokémon to discover at every turn and rare Ultra Beasts to study in these pages packed with puzzles, quizzes and brain teasers.

You'll need wisdom to rival the Rotom Dex and the bravery of an Island Kahuna on your quest to become a great Trainer ... read on to begin your journey. Only once you've completed all the challenges will you earn your own extraordinary Z-Ring, just like Ash.

Good luck, Trainer!

SCHOOL DAYS

Ash is starting at the Pokémon School on Melemele Island. Solve the riddle to give Professor Kukui the info he needs to enrol his new pupil.

My first is in KIAWE
and also in MUK.

My second is in GRIMER
but never in GRUBBIN.

My third is in LITTEN
and also in TORRACAT.

My fourth is in CUBONE
but never in BOUNSWEET.

My fifth is in ASH but
never in FOMANTIS.

My sixth is in YUNGOOS
and also in TRUMBEAK.

My seventh is in MUDBRAY
and also in GOLEM.

**When you've
solved the riddle,
write it below:**

PIKACHU PUZZLER

It's a Pikachu storm! How many Pokémon can you count altogether?
Tick the box with the correct number.

29 ☐   26 ☐   28 ☐

WHAT'S MY TYPE?

Now tick the box to show which type of Pokémon Pikachu is.

Fire ☐   Fighting ☐   Electric ☐

7

SPLASH ZONE

Starting at the letter A, help Lana swim through the grid in alphabetical order to reach her Water-type Pokémon.

	A	R	L	I	M	Q
	B	F	V	B	E	D
K	F	C	N	S	T	U	V
T	W	D	X	R	C	B	W
G	F	E	A	Q	B	Y	X
H	W	S	Z	P	V	Z	O
I	Y	M	N	O	C		
J	K	L	U	S	X		

WHO'S THAT POKÉMON?

Popplio evolves twice! Fill in the missing letters to complete the names of the two evolved Pokémon.

B _ 1 0 _ _ E   P _ _ M R _ _ A

ROTOM REVEAL

Starting at number 1, join the dots in order to reveal a useful companion to Ash on his adventures in Alola.

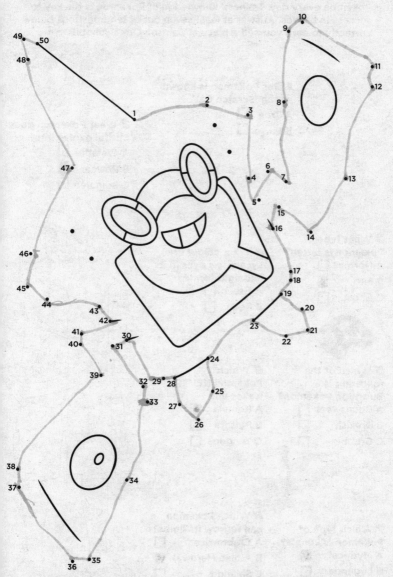

PRINCIPAL OAK'S TEST

The students at the Pokémon School on Melemele Island study Pokémon every day. Trainers' knowledge of Pokémon is the key to success in battles. Answer at least seven out of ten questions below correctly to earn yourself a place at Samson Oak's school!

1 This Pokémon is known as the 'Scratch Cat'.
A True ☐
B False ☐

2 What Pokémon does Stufful evolve into?
A Clefable ☐
B Bewear ☑
C Solgaleo ☐

3 What type of Pokémon is Litten?
A Normal ☐
B Fire ☑
C Ghost ☐

4 What colour are Lycanroc's eyes in its Midnight form?
A Green ☐
B Red ☐

5 Which of the following is a Bug-type Pokémon?
A Bounsweet ☐
B Bruxish ☐
C Grubbin ☐

6 Which Pokémon NEVER wakes up?
A Komala ☑
B Rattata ☐
C Yungoos ☐

7 Which type of Pokémon is Lunala?
A Mythical ☑
B Legendary ☐

8 Which Pokémon can regrow its limbs?
A Crabrawler ☐
B Alolan Marowak ☑
C Salandit ☐

TRAINERS BEWARE!

Stufful, a Normal- and Fighting-type Pokémon evolves into something far less cute! Discover the name of the evolved Pokémon by finding its name hidden in this forest maze. Find your way to the finish, collecting only the letters directly on your path.

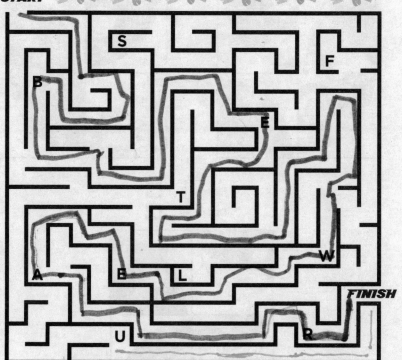

Stufful evolves into:

___ ___ ___ ___ ___ ___ ___ ___

11

TEAM SKULL SWITCH

Team Skull have mixed up the Poké Balls that Ash needs to help him catch some rare Pokémon. Can you work out which type of Poké Ball each one is? Tick the box each time.

1 Quick Ball ☐

Luxury Ball ☐

2 Ultra Ball ☐

Dive Ball ☐

3 Repeat Ball ☐

Dusk Ball ☐

NEW FACES

Litten and Popplio are just two faces that Ash and Pikachu have met on their travels in Alola. Look at these Pokémon patterns, then write or draw the missing Pokémon in each row.

1 Pikachu — Rotom Dex — **popplio** (?) — Pikachu — Rotom Dex — Popplio

2 Rowlet — Litten — Popplio — ? — Litten — Popplio

3 ? — Pikachu — Pikachu — Rowlet — Rowlet — Rowlet

4 Pikachu — Meowth — Pikachu — Meowth — Pikachu — ?

5 Rotom Dex — Rotom Dex — ? — Rotom Dex — Rotom Dex — Litten

13

TEAMING UP

Team Rocket cause trouble at every turn! Guide Jessie and James through the maze to help them team up with the Pokémon they need to take on Ash and Pikachu.

Mareanie

START

Bewear

Mimikyu

Mimikyu ☐
Bewear ☐
Mareanie ☐
Wobbuffet ☐

Wobbuffet

FINISH

CATCH OF THE DAY

DIFFICULTY:

Poké Balls are used to catch and store Pokémon and come in loads of cool designs. Can you change the word 'HEAL' into 'BALL' in just five steps? At each step change just one letter to make a new word, without rearranging any of the letters. For example, you could start by changing MIND to MINT. Use the clues to help you.

H E A L
B A L L

Clues:

Something that actually exists and is not imagined.

To fasten or close something securely.

To give or trade something in exchange for money.

An instrument that makes a ringing sound.

FUNNY FEELINGS

Draw a line to match each sentence with a Pikachu face to show how Ash's little buddy is feeling.

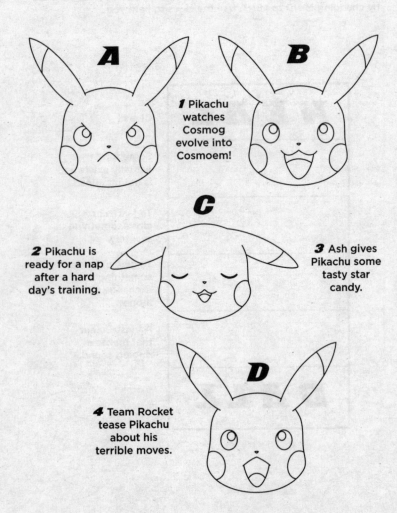

A

B

1 Pikachu watches Cosmog evolve into Cosmoem!

C

2 Pikachu is ready for a nap after a hard day's training.

3 Ash gives Pikachu some tasty star candy.

D

4 Team Rocket tease Pikachu about his terrible moves.

EXPLORING AKALA

Akala Island is home to a host of cool Pokémon! Find their names – plus Ash and Pikachu's – in the puzzle below. The words read forwards, backwards, up, down and diagonally.

U	G	N	H	S	T	U	F	F	U	L	K	M	U	W
Z	T	C	C	U	J	D	R	H	W	Q	T	S	T	R
W	A	L	O	L	A	N	M	A	R	O	W	A	K	B
R	L	A	L	M	W	C	J	K	S	T	L	N	I	Y
E	J	Q	R	B	F	M	D	M	B	H	G	D	A	N
S	U	G	R	T	K	E	S	Y	C	O	J	Y	W	T
M	C	T	P	D	P	G	Y	N	Z	R	B	G	X	E
B	H	Z	I	S	Q	I	T	G	R	A	Q	A	H	L
P	Y	U	K	U	M	U	K	U	L	N	C	S	M	E
C	U	B	A	L	U	B	I	I	H	G	L	T	C	L
T	N	M	C	Z	J	S	A	W	P	E	U	W	Q	U
Y	G	P	H	K	H	K	W	L	Q	E	G	M	Z	P
U	O	T	U	C	Q	J	E	U	S	N	K	K	R	A
Q	O	P	W	J	Z	B	T	W	H	P	B	H	G	T
A	S	K	G	O	R	A	N	G	U	R	U	Z	U	V

ASH   TAPU LELE   COMFEY   SANDYGAST

PIKACHU   PYUKUMUKU   ORANGURU   PIKIPEK

KIAWE   YUNGOOS   STUFFUL   ALOLAN
                                        MAROWAK

ISLAND KAHUNA

Rearrange the letters in grey to discover an Island Kahuna. Is it:

Nanu ☐   Halu ☐   Olivia ☐   Hapu ☐

17

CHANGING CREATURES

Things are forever changing in the Alola region – especially the Pokémon that live there! Professor Kukui has mixed up these Evolution chains. Write the letters in the boxes to show the order in which the Pokémon evolve.

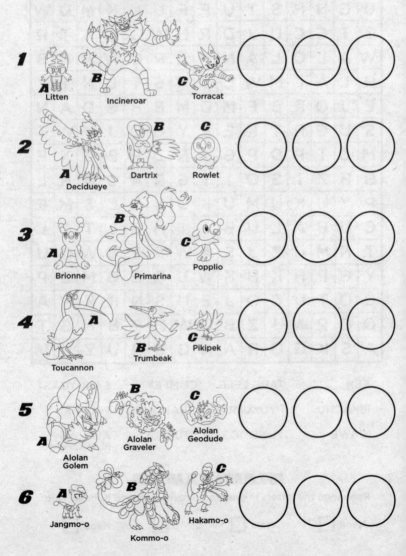

1

A Litten
B Incineroar
C Torracat

( ) ( ) ( )

2

A Decidueye
B Dartrix
C Rowlet

( ) ( ) ( )

3

A Brionne
B Primarina
C Popplio

( ) ( ) ( )

4

A Toucannon
B Trumbeak
C Pikipek

( ) ( ) ( )

5

A Alolan Golem
B Alolan Graveler
C Alolan Geodude

( ) ( ) ( )

6

A Jangmo-o
B Kommo-o
C Hakamo-o

( ) ( ) ( )

POKÉMON PALS

One of these Pokémon always has bags of energy, while the other is the sleepiest creature in the Alola region! Follow the lines to reveal which Pokémon likes to hang out with Professor Kukui and which one pairs up with Principal Oak.

Komala

Rockruff

Professor Kukui

Principal Samson Oak

BROKEN BALL

Ash's Poké Ball smashed when a Crabominable broke free!
Put the Poké Ball pieces back together by copying the shapes
exactly into the space below. Caution: one piece doesn't fit,
circle the Poké Ball piece you don't need.

MATES MAZE

Time how long it takes you to guide Ash and Pikachu through this tricky Poké Ball maze to reach their Trainer friends on the other side. Can you find the finish in less than two minutes?

START

FINISH

FAMOUS FOUR

Each of the major islands of Alola has its own guardian spirit. Unscramble the word next to each guardian to reveal the island it watches over.

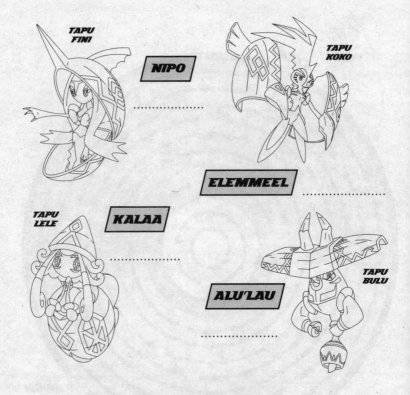

TAPU FINI

NIPO

....

TAPU KOKO

ELEMMEEL

....

TAPU LELE

KALAA

....

ALU'LAU

....

TAPU BULU

QUICK QUIZ

Now answer these questions about the island spirits.
Use the pictures to help you.

1 Which guardian stores electricity beneath its wings? ....

2 Whose horns can cause heavy destruction? ....

3 Which guardian gains energy from the ocean? ....

4 Which fluttering guardian possesses healing scales? ....

POWER CUT

When Blacephalon the Fireworks Pokémon appeared on Melemele Island, it absorbed all the electricity in the area! Help Ash and his friends track down the Ultra Beast and reconnect the power.
Fill in the missing numbers from 1 to 25 in order, then trace a path to complete the electrical circuit. The path uses only horizontal and vertical lines.

Example solution:

8	7	4	3
9	6	5	2
10	13	14	1
11	12	15	16

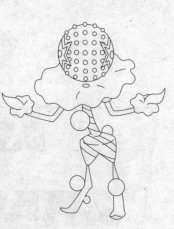

5	6	21	22	25
	7		23	
	8	19		
2		12	13	16
1	10		14	

23

MIRROR, MIRROR...

Lusamine has sent a coded message to Ash and his friends. Can you work out what it says? Clue: decode the message in reverse!

ULTRA GUARDIANS, TO THE BASE!

....

....

LUNCH DATE

There are eight differences between these lunchtime scenes. Can you spot them all? Colour in a Berry for each difference you find.

POKÉMON POWER!

 DIFFICULTY:

Smart Sophocles often uses Electric-type Pokémon to power his inventions! Look at the close-ups, then fill in the missing letters to complete the names of his Pokémon pals.

1 T _ _ e d _ m _ _ _

2 _ _ _ _ r j _ _ _ _ _

3 _ l o _ _ _
   _ _ _ c _ u

4 _ _ k _ v _ _ t

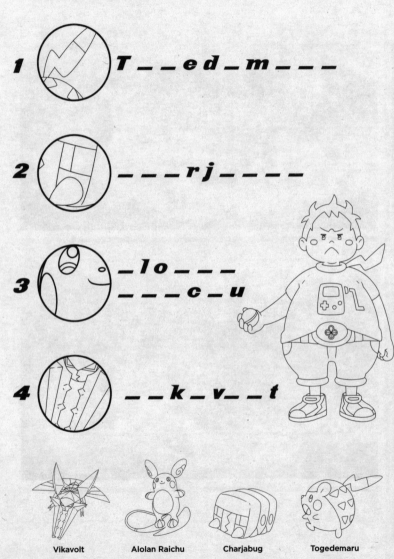

Vikavolt   Alolan Raichu   Charjabug   Togedemaru

26

SUPER SUDOKU

Draw pictures in the grids so that each column and each row contains only one of each symbol.

Puzzle 1:
EASY

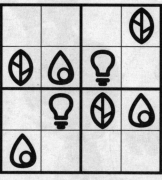

Puzzle 2:
TOUGH

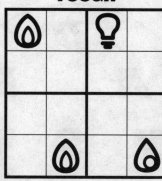
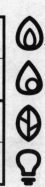

Puzzle 3:
SUPER TOUGH

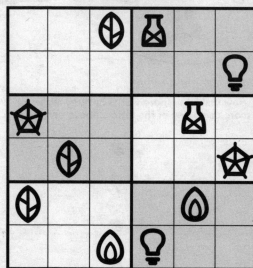

IN THE SHADOWS

DIFFICULTY: ●─◇─●

There have been so few sightings of this rare Fighting- and Ghost-type Pokémon that Trainers can't be sure whether it really exists. Rearrange the letters below, using each letter only once to reveal the name of this shadowy Pokémon.

D
A   R
W   S   M
H   O
A

....

Now make ten more words of three letters or more using any of the letters above only once.

1 ....
2 ....
3 ....
4 ....
5 ....

6 ....
7 ....
8 ....
9 ....
10 ....

GUESS THE GUARDIAN

Join the dots to meet Melemele Island's curious Electric- and Fairy-type guardian.

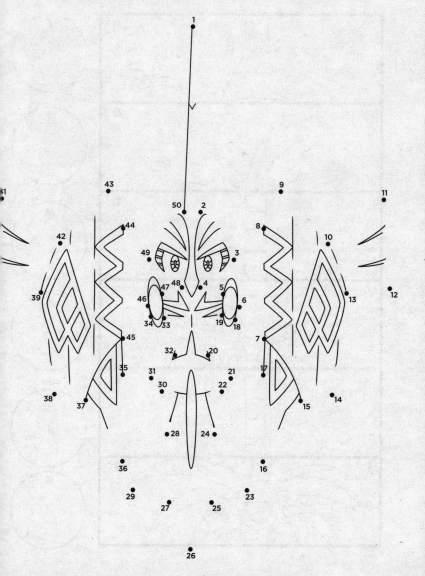

GROWING PAINS

DIFFICULTY: ●

Did you know that an Alolan Exeggutor can grow to over 10 metres tall? This towering Pokémon is looking a little mixed up – can you piece it back together in the right order?

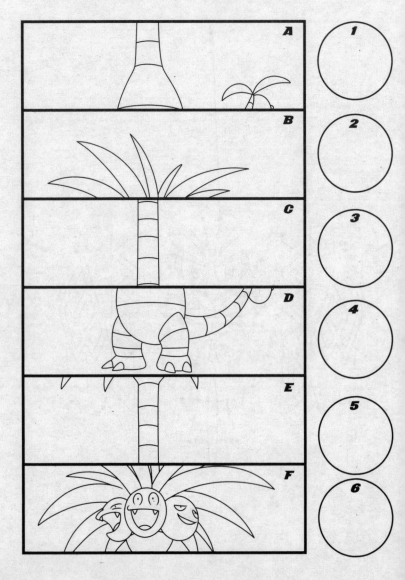

GOT THE BUG

The Alola region is home to a whole bunch of Bug-type Pokémon! Find each beastly bug in the grid below. The names read forwards, backwards, up, down and diagonally.

R	P	O	A	Q	U	A	R	A	Q	U	A	N	I	D
J	I	W	Q	R	T	L	S	H	X	K	G	F	X	J
U	F	B	Y	B	G	M	K	N	M	V	O	E	Q	N
D	C	U	O	C	R	W	C	J	E	F	L	Z	U	L
S	H	Z	J	M	U	V	U	D	T	R	I	Y	D	F
R	P	G	S	V	B	F	T	C	A	J	S	V	C	G
W	Q	X	E	R	B	E	I	B	P	M	O	H	P	U
H	D	F	D	P	I	J	E	R	O	D	P	X	K	B
V	O	S	W	Q	N	X	F	W	D	R	O	B	V	A
F	P	E	Y	D	U	R	L	U	E	K	D	J	Z	J
B	M	V	N	M	J	N	Y	Z	Y	D	Z	W	D	R
X	I	C	A	T	E	R	P	I	E	F	J	I	H	A
L	W	R	D	K	P	M	J	H	C	W	V	C	Z	H
I	D	K	C	W	Y	Q	Y	M	R	V	D	U	X	C
T	R	B	U	F	T	L	O	V	A	K	I	V	J	S

CHARJABUG   RIBOMBEE   METAPOD   GOLISOPOD
CUTIEFLY   VIKAVOLT   CATERPIE
GRUBBIN   WIMPOD   ARAQUANID

WHO'S THAT POKÉMON?

One little critter is feeling shy! Write down the shaded letters, then unscramble them to work out who it is.

....

Is the Pokémon WIMPOD ☐   or DEWPIDER ☐ ?

MASTER OF DISGUISE

Shade the shapes with a dot to reveal a Pokémon that's a sneaky shape-shifter.

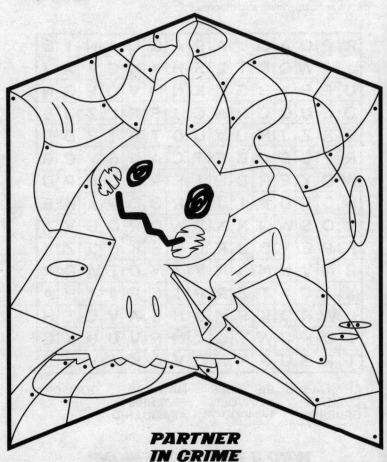

PARTNER IN CRIME

Now tick the member of Team Rocket that the Pokémon partners.

Jessie ☐   James ☐

ULTRA SCRAMBLE

DIFFICULTY:

Time for your toughest test yet, Trainer! Unscramble the names of these Ultra Beasts, writing the letters in the correct order in the boxes. Then take the circled letters to reveal a secret Ultra Beast who's a friend to Ash and Pikachu.

1 ERSHAMPOO

_ _ _ _ _ _ _ _ _ _

2 DROZZLUG

_ _ _ _ _ _ _ _ _

3 OLIIGHENI

_ _ _ _ _ _ _ _ _

4 ALPOBLANCHE

_ _ _ _ _ _ _ _ _ _ _

5 ANDANGELA

_ _ _ _ _ _ _ _ _

6 REETRIXUK

The secret Ultra Beast is:

_ _ _ _ _ _ _ _ _

○ ○ ○ ○ ○ ○ ○

FREQUENT FLYERS

DIFFICULTY: 🔴

Draw lines to make pairs of Flying-type Pokémon. One Pokémon does not have a match – do you know why?

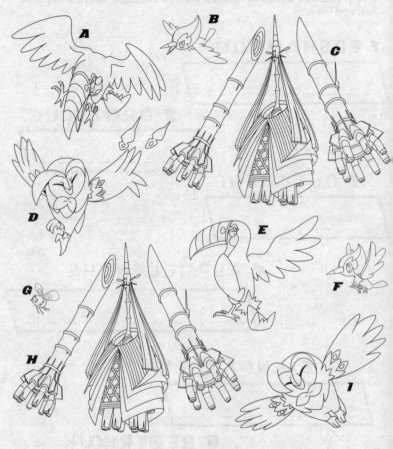

The odd one out is:

....

because

....

FALSE FRIENDS

Begin at the START, then follow the path passing only true Pokémon types. Avoid the pretend Pokémon types to quickly reach the finish.

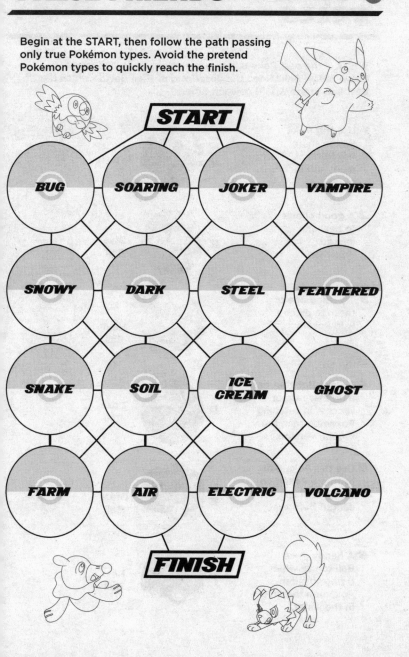

START

BUG	SOARING	JOKER	VAMPIRE
SNOWY	DARK	STEEL	FEATHERED
SNAKE	SOIL	ICE CREAM	GHOST
FARM	AIR	ELECTRIC	VOLCANO

FINISH

PUZZLING POKÉ BALLS

Which is the best Poké Ball to use at night and when might you throw a Heal Ball? Read the descriptions, then decide which the best ball to use would be each time.

1 Use this Poké Ball to snare Pokémon at night and in caves.

A Repeat Ball

2 A good choice to heal an injured Pokémon.

B Dive Ball

3 Try using one of these to catch a wild Pokémon.

C Heal Ball

4 A Poké Ball that has a greater rate of success in catching Pokémon than the regular version.

D Dusk Ball

5 Use this Poké Ball to trap a Pokémon that has been caught before.

E Great Ball

6 A handy Poké Ball to use when trying to catch Pokémon that live in the water.

F  Nest Ball

MIND BLOWN!

Which power-loving Ultra Beast is having a blast below? Rearrange the picture to reveal the answer.

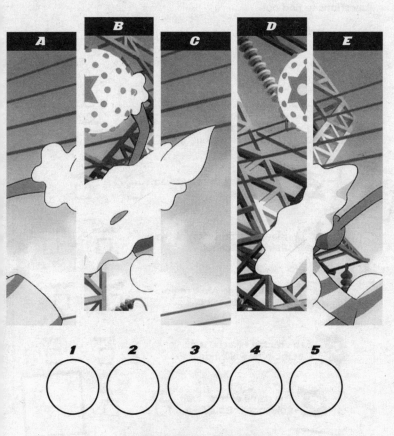

ANOTHER NAME

This Ultra Beast is also known as:

1 The Fireworks Pokémon. ☐

2 The Pyrotechnics Pokémon. ☐

3 The Exploding Pokémon. ☐

TRAINER TEST

Think you'd make a top Trainer? Answer true or false to Professor Kukui's tricky questions to find out.

1 The Rock-type Pokémon, Stakataka, looks like a stone wall.

True ☐   False ☐

2 Tapu Bulu is the Guardian of Akala Island.

True ☐   False ☐

3 Kiawe is a professor at the Pokémon School.

True ☐   False ☐

4 Berries in the Alola region always taste salty.

True ☐   False ☐

5 Ash's buddy Pikachu is an Electric-type Pokémon.

True ☐   False ☐

6 The name of this Pokémon is Bounsour.

True ☐   False ☐

7 This Poké Ball is known as a Bee Ball.

True ☐   False ☐

8 A Z-Ring is needed if a Trainer is to perform Z-Moves.

True ☐   False ☐

POISON PAL

This playful Ultra Beast is a friend to Ash and Pikachu! Join the dots to reveal the Poison-type Pokémon.

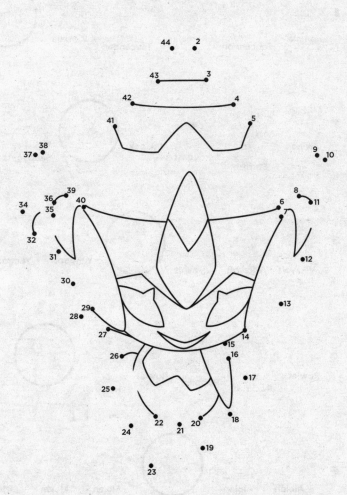

The Pokémon is: ....

PROBLEM PATTERNS

Check out these pretty Pokémon patterns! Write the name of the Pokémon that's missing from each row or try drawing them.

1

Komala   Toucannon   Komala   Toucannon   Komala

....

2

Pikipek   Sandygast   Pikipek   Sandygast

Stufful

....

3

Vikavolt   Vikavolt   Vikavolt   Yungoos   Yungoos

....

4

Rowlet   Popplio   Rowlet

Rockruff   Rockruff

....

5

Alolan Muk   Alolan Muk   Alolan Muk   Alolan Muk   Litten

....

ULTRA TEST

Place all of the listed Ultra Beasts into the grid, once each, so that they read either across or down with one letter per box. Tip: try placing the Ultra Beasts with longer names first.

7 LETTER BEASTS
Poipole
Kartana

8 LETTER BEASTS
Guzzlord
Buzzwole
Nihilego

9 LETTER BEASTS
Xurkitree
Pheromosa

10 LETTER BEASTS
Celesteela

11 LETTER BEASTS
Blacephalon

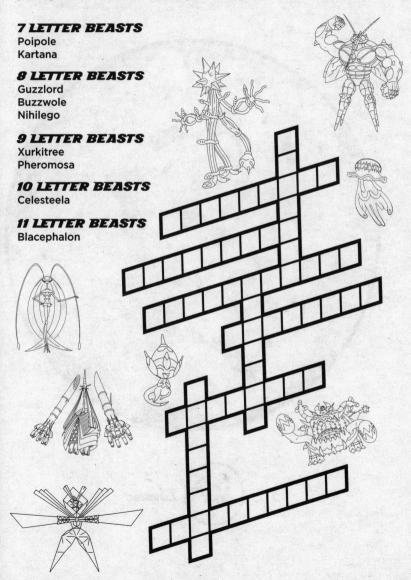

WATER WATCH

DIFFICULTY: 🔴

Quickly count the number of Luvdisc in the school below and write the number in the box. They're the sweethearts of the seas!

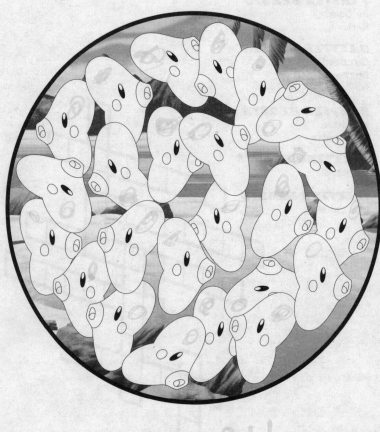

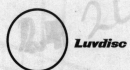

Luvdisc

WEB WEAVER

The long-legged Ariados spinning a web is an awesome sight.
Use the colour code to help you brighten up this Bug- and
Poison-type Pokémon.

1 = **RED**   3 = **PURPLE**
2 = **BLACK**   4 = **YELLOW**
          5 = **GREY**

SPECIES SWITCH

There are many Pokémon types that can combine to create some special species. Try to change the word 'DARK' into 'ROCK' in just five steps. You must change just one letter at a time without rearranging any of the letters. Read the clues to help you.

D A R K
R O C K

Clues:

A noise a Rockruff might make.

A building where money is stored.

To sort things in order of your favourite.

A frame that holds or stores things.

BONUS BALLS

Now write down the names of these Pokémon and tick their type for a bonus score.

Dark-type ☐
Rock-type ☐

Dark-type ☐
Rock-type ☐

CRISS CROSS

How many of these puzzling Pokémon clues can you work out?
Complete the crossword to become a true Pokémon champion!

ACROSS

1 The Pokémon School is situated on this Alolan island. (8)

5 This Fire-type Pokémon spits red-hot furballs. (6)

7 The guardian deity of Akala Island. (4, 4)

8 The first name of Principal Oak, Professor Oak's cousin. (6)

9 Use this Poké Ball to catch a Pokémon at night or in the dark. (4, 4)

10 Stuful evolves into this Fighting-type Pokémon. (6)

DOWN

2 This cosmic creature is the largest Legendary Pokémon in the Alola region. (6)

3 The name of Ash's best buddy. Easy! (7)

4 The colour of Water-type Pokémon, Popplio. (4)

6 Kiawe's devasting Pokémon with a super-hard shell. (10)

PONI PUZZLE

 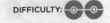

Find the Pokémon on Poni Island and write down their coordinates.
Pikachu is in square D3.

PIKACHU

RIBOMBEE

KOMMO-O

ASH

TAPU FINI

JANGMO-O

SLEEPY SIDEKICK

Read the clues to figure out which Pokémon features in this riddle. Can you reveal Principal Oak's dreamy friend?

My first is in PIKACHU but never in PICHU.

My second is in KOKO but never in TAPU.

My third is in MINIOR and also in MUK.

My fourth is in ASH and also in ALOLA.

My fifth is in LILLIE and also in MALLOW.

My sixth is in GREAT and also in BALL.

When you've solved the riddle, write the answer below:

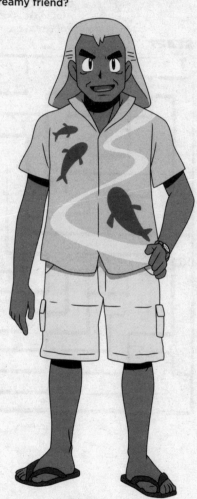

....

RISKY ROUTE

Help Ash and Pikachu travel safely through this maze on Akala Island. Watch out for Alolan Geodudes along their path – these Pokémon are highly charged!

START

FINISH

I CHOOSE YOU!

Which of Kiawe's partner Pokémon will he choose to contest his next Pokémon battle? Complete the key, then crack the code to find out!

A	B	C	D	E	F	G	H	I	J	K	L	M
1		3	4		6			9	10		12	

N	O	P	Q	R	S	T	U	V	W	X	Y	Z
14	15			19			22		24			

_ _ _ _ _ _ _ _ _ _

20 21 18 20 15 14 1 20 15 18

Tick the box when you've worked out the answer:

Charizard ☐   **Alolan Marowak** ☐   **Turtonator** ☐

POWERED UP

Draw the other half of Necrozma after it has absorbed the light of Solgaleo, then identify the new Pokémon.

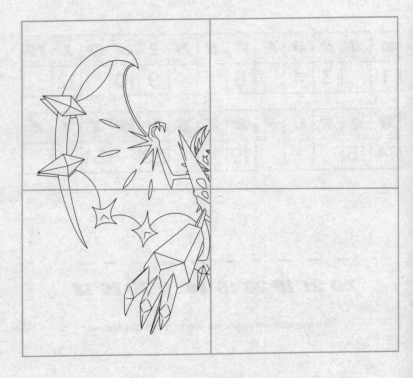

D _ _ _ W _ _ _ _

Necrozma

ALOLA TRAVELS

How well do you know the Alola region? Find the names of each location hidden in the grid below. The names read forwards, backwards, up, down and diagonally.

Q	J	R	B	W	R	T	S	J	E	F	M	T	U	O	Q	P	P	H	U
Y	X	M	A	L	A	K	A	I	G	Y	N	E	A	Q	K	N	A	L	Q
U	Z	H	E	S	D	O	K	C	A	E	O	N	P	I	C	U	L	X	E
L	U	P	F	M	M	U	E	Z	L	V	Y	C	N	Y	O	F	M	P	B
A	X	N	L	X	O	N	O	Y	L	T	M	A	P	L	F	N	M	N	T
U	I	S	J	F	C	R	A	T	I	L	L	R	I	M	T	U	S	A	P
L	M	N	T	D	Z	H	I	C	V	U	P	A	B	D	H	O	P	U	G
A	E	E	O	Y	S	F	E	A	K	T	Q	T	J	K	X	U	B	Q	B
Q	L	B	L	P	L	I	P	O	L	N	L	H	O	T	V	A	I	Y	M
B	G	N	Q	E	L	B	H	U	O	H	E	I	I	I	H	O	V	R	E
D	N	Q	U	A	M	T	R	K	F	Q	I	L	L	P	Y	X	S	Z	J
A	U	H	M	U	N	E	M	D	A	T	I	L	P	F	T	V	U	O	Z
O	J	O	U	U	D	U	L	A	E	D	A	B	L	H	A	Z	G	W	B
O	H	N	O	K	T	A	Z	E	S	G	H	A	N	O	B	E	A	C	H
V	S	M	F	Q	T	R	E	S	E	D	A	N	I	A	H	G	Q	B	M
X	U	M	K	Z	C	C	F	A	R	H	W	H	G	Q	B	S	S	T	R
D	L	V	B	L	U	S	H	M	O	U	N	T	A	I	N	A	O	Y	R

MELEMELE
AKALA
ULAULA
PONI
TAPU VILLAGE
HAUOLI
MALIE CITY
MEMORIAL HILL
LUSH JUNGLE
HAINA DESERT
TEN CARAT HILL
HANO BEACH
MOUNT HOKULANI
BLUSH MOUNTAIN
SEAFOLK VILLAGE

ON THE DOUBLE

The students at the Pokémon School are studying a darting Dewpider, a Water- and Bug-type Pokémon. Spot eight differences between the pictures, then colour in a Poké Ball for each one you spot.

HATS OFF!

Can you guess which Pokémon has cheekily borrowed Ash's hat?
Join the dots to find out!

The password to Professor Kukui's computer matches the name of a Grass- and Flying-type Pokémon. Can you work out the six-letter word by using each letter only once to spell out the word?

Once you've found the word, write a list of more words that can be made using the letters only once. Make 15 words of two or more letters to pass the test.

__ __ __ __ __ __

....

....

....

....

....

SNACK TIME

DIFFICULTY: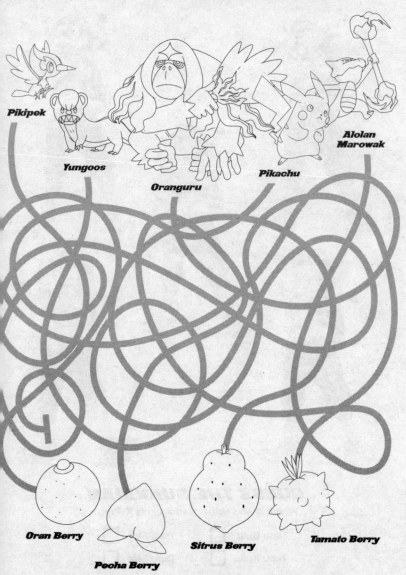

Trace the lines to discover which Pokémon from Akala Island is snacking on which juicy Berry. Then find the Pokémon that will go hungry!

Pikipek

Yungoos

Oranguru

Pikachu

Alolan Marowak

Oran Berry

Pecha Berry

Sitrus Berry

Tamato Berry

ASH IMPOSTERS

DIFFICULTY:

These pictures of Ash Ketchum may look the same but only one of them is the true Trainer – circle the real Ash.

GUESS THE GUARDIAN
Which island spirit gave Ash his Z-Ring?

Tapu Bulu ☐   Tapu Fini ☐

Tapu Koko ☐   Tapu Lele ☐

ISLAND PATH

Help Ash and his Pokémon through the maze to visit Ula'ula's Island Guardian, Tapu Bulu. Find four other Pokémon along the way.

Crabominable ☐

Mudsdale ☐

Vikavolt ☐

Mimikyu ☐

Tapu Bulu ☐

NUMBER CRUNCH

DIFFICULTY: ◐◐

Things just aren't adding up for Ash. Can you help him? Finish filling in the numbers from 1 to 9 in the Poké Balls so that the sum of the numbers on each side of a triangle is always 17.

GOING GREEN

Don't let the grass grow, Trainer! Unscramble the names of these Grass-type Pokémon, writing the letters in the correct order in the boxes. Then take the shaded letters to reveal a secret Pokémon that makes a perfect partner for Mallow.

CHINOSITI

⬡ ◯ ◯ ◯ ◯ ◯ ◯ ◯ ◯

ATOMFINS

◯ ◯ ◯ ◯ ◯ ⬡ ◯ ◯

CUDEYEDIE

◯ ⬡ ◯ ◯ ◯ ◯ ◯ ◯ ◯

ERLWOT

◯ ◯ ◯ ◯ ⬡ ◯

BENOWTSUE

◯ ◯ ◯ ⬡ ◯ ◯ ◯ ◯ ◯

EARNATSE

◯ ◯ ◯ ◯ ◯ ⬡ ◯ ◯

MULEROLL

◯ ◯ ◯ ⬡ ◯ ◯ ◯ ◯

The secret Grass-type Pokémon is:

⬡ ⬡ ⬡ ⬡ ⬡ ⬡ ⬡

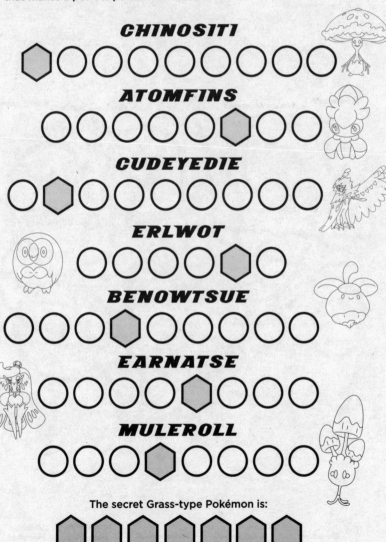

59

TIME FOR A CHANGE

DIFFICULTY:

These awesome Alolan Pokémon evolve into even cooler Formes!
Follow the lines to discover the Evolutions.

Rockruff   Alolan Meowth   Stufful   Alolan Vulpix   Sandygast

Bewear   Alolan Ninetales   Palossand   Lycanroc (Midday Form)   Alolan Persian

TYPE TEASER

Does your brain store information like Rotom Dex or do you frequently forget things like Principal Oak? Test your memory by connecting each Pokémon with the correct type. Can you match all eight?

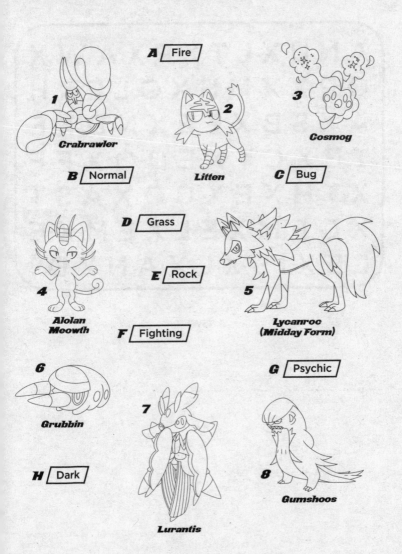

A Fire

1 Crabrawler

2 Litten

3 Cosmog

B Normal

C Bug

D Grass

4 Alolan Meowth

E Rock

5 Lycanroc (Midday Form)

F Fighting

G Psychic

6 Grubbin

7 Lurantis

8 Gumshoos

H Dark

DIFFICULTY:

Professor Burnet has sent the Ultra Guardians a message. There's just one problem – the message has been scrambled. Scribble out the letter X every time it appears to reveal Burnet's important news.

```
A N U X L T X R X A W X
O R X X M H X O L E X H
A X S B X E E X N D X E
T E X C T X E D O X F F
X T H X E X C O X A S T
X O F M X E L X E M X E
L E X I S X L X A N X D .
```

ANSWER:

....

....

....

CRITTER COUNT

DIFFICULTY:

Ash has been busy catching every new Pokémon he meets on his travels in Alola! Study the picture carefully and write down how many of each Pokémon Ash has caught.

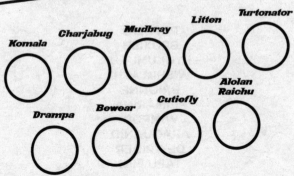

Komala

Charjabug

Mudbray

Litten

Turtonator

Drampa

Bewear

Cutiefly

Alolan Raichu

KEEPING COOL

The Alola region is home to some cool creatures that love to hang out in the tropical waters there. Find ten Water-type Pokémon in the wordsearch below.

D	I	N	A	U	Q	A	R	A	P	L	O	I	B	Z
N	R	V	B	L	Q	N	I	R	V	I	V	X	N	L
W	Z	E	A	R	U	W	I	W	L	B	X	F	D	P
I	I	Y	D	C	I	M	J	P	I	J	S	B	B	E
V	Q	S	X	I	A	O	P	D	S	P	U	E	K	X
O	A	Q	H	R	P	O	N	D	J	Y	M	I	T	N
E	Z	O	I	I	P	W	J	N	A	U	W	N	C	O
N	J	N	Q	V	W	C	E	T	E	K	P	I	Z	X
Q	A	B	J	O	S	A	D	D	P	U	P	F	N	C
S	O	U	Z	I	F	P	S	M	E	M	X	U	F	W
A	W	I	V	Z	X	L	T	H	L	U	A	P	U	I
M	W	P	U	E	H	K	M	V	I	K	M	A	V	M
O	A	T	U	O	P	P	P	E	R	U	W	T	P	P
D	K	B	A	B	G	X	N	R	H	F	M	I	X	O
Y	Y	B	R	U	X	I	S	H	O	R	L	K	G	D

POPPLIO
BRUXISH
PYUKUMUKU
WISHIWASHI
BRIONNE
PRIMARINA
WIMPOD
ARAQUANID
DEWPIDER
TAPU FINI

CHALLENGES COMPLETE!

Only once you've completed all the puzzles in this book will you earn your own Z-Ring, just like Ash and Kiawe! It will bring you strength in Pokémon battles and help you perform awesome Z-Moves, too. Join the dots to reveal the ring.

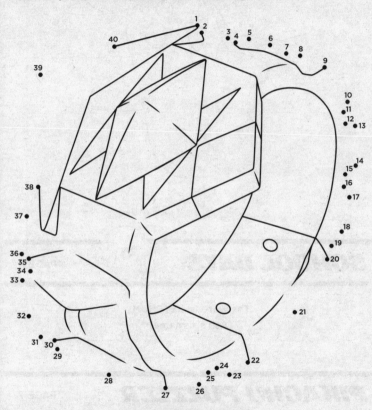

ODD MOVE OUT

Four of the following are battle-winning Z-Moves, but one is a fake!
Tick the real moves and cross the odd one out.

Gigavolt Havoc ☐   Continental Crush ☐

Breakneck Blitz ☐   Underground Undercook ☐

Splintered Stormshards ☐

SOLUTIONS

SCHOOL DAYS

PAGE 6

The word is: KETCHUM
(Ash's surname)

PIKACHU PUZZLER

PAGE 7

There are 28 Pikachus.

Pikachu is an Electric-type Pokémon.

SPLASH ZONE

	A	R	L	I	M	Q
	B	F	V	B	E	D
K	F	C	N	S	T	U	V
T	W	D	X	R	C	B	W
G	F	E	A	Q	B	Y	X
H	W	S	Z	P	V	Z	O
I	Y	M	N	O	C		
J	K	L	U	S	X		

WHO'S THAT POKÉMON?

Brionne

Primarina

ROTOM REVEAL

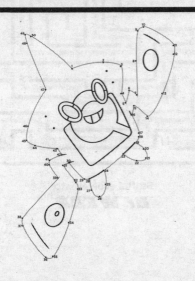

PRINCIPAL OAK'S TEST

PAGE 10

1. A – True,
2. B – Bewear,
3. B – Fire,
4. B – Red,
5. C – Grubbin,

6. A – Komala,
7. B – Legendary,
8. A – Crabrawler.

TRAINERS BEWARE!

PAGE 11

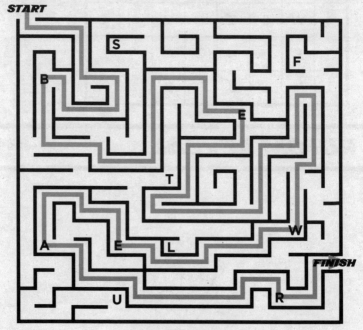

Stufful evolves into:

BEWEAR

1 Quick Ball ☑
Luxury Ball ☐

2 Ultra Ball ☐
Dive Ball ☑

3 Repeat Ball ☑
Dusk Ball ☐

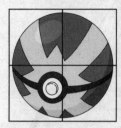

1
 Pikachu
 Rotom Dex
 Popplio
 Pikachu
 Rotom Dex
Popplio

2
 Rowlet
 Litten
 Popplio
 Rowlet
 Litten
 Popplio

3
 Pikachu
 Pikachu
 Pikachu
 Rowlet
 Rowlet
Rowlet

4
 Pikachu
 Meowth
 Pikachu
 Meowth
Pikachu
Meowth

5
 Rotom Dex
 Rotom Dex
 Litten
 Rotom Dex
 Rotom Dex
 Litten

START

Dreanie

Mimikyu

Wobbuffet

FINISH

CATCH OF THE DAY PAGE 15

HEAL
REAL
SEAL
SELL
BELL
BALL

FUNNY FEELINGS

PAGE 16

1 – D, 2 – C, 3 – B, 4 – A.

EXPLORING AKALA

PAGE 17

The Island Kahuna is
OLIVIA

CHANGING CREATURES PAGE 18

1. A, C, B.
2. C, B, A.
3. C, A, B.

4. C, B, A.
5. C, B, A.
6. A, C, B.

POKÉMON PALS

BROKEN BALL

Piece D is not needed.

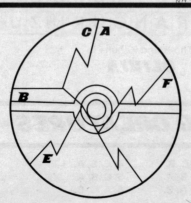

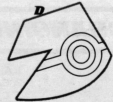

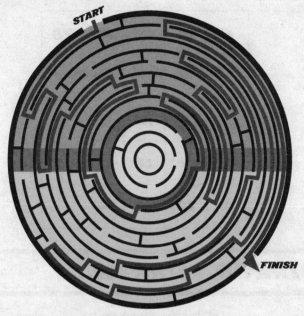

START

FINISH

FAMOUS FOUR

PAGE 22

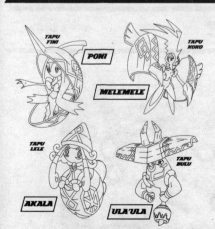

TAPU FINI

PONI

TAPU KOKO

MELEMELE

TAPU LELE

AKALA

ULA'ULA

TAPU BULU

QUICK QUIZ
1. Tapu Koko
2. Tapu Bulu
3. Tapu Fini
4. Tapu Lele

POWER CUT

PAGE 23

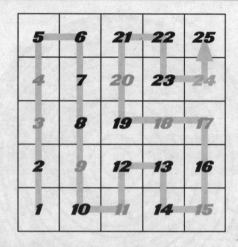

MIRROR, MIRROR...

PAGE 24

Lusamine's message reads:

ULTRA GUARDIANS, TO THE BASE!

LUNCH DATE

PAGE 25

POKÉMON POWER

PAGE 26

1. Togedemaru, 2. Charjabug, 3. Alolan Raichu, 4. Vikavolt.

SUPER SUDOKU

PAGE 27

Puzzle 1:

Puzzle 2:

Puzzle 3:

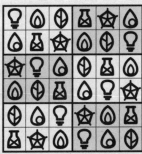

IN THE SHADOWS

PAGE 28

**The Pokémon is
MARSHADOW.**

**Some of the words that can
be made include:**
ADO, ARM(S), AROMA(S),
ASH, AWARD(S), AWASH,
DAM(S), DASH, DORM(S),
DOSH, DRAMA(S), DRAW(S),
HAD, HAM, HARD, HARM(S),
HAS, HOARD(S), HOW, MAD,
MARSH, MOD(S), MOSH, MOW,
MRS, OAR, RAD, RAM, ROAD(S),
ROAM(S), ROD(S), ROW, SAD,
SHADOW, SHARD, SHOW,
SODA, SOW, SWAM, SWARM,
SWORD, WAD(S), WAR(S),
WARD(S), WHAM, WORD(S)

GUESS THE GUARDIAN

PAGE 29

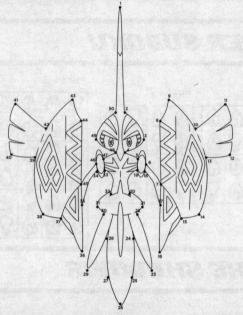

GROWING PAINS

PAGE 30

1 – B
2 – F
3 – E
4 – C
5 – A
6 – D

R	P	O	A	Q	U	A	R	A	Q	U	A	N	I	D
J	I	W	Q	R	T	L	S	H	X	K	G	F	X	J
U	F	B	Y	B	G	M	K	N	M	V	O	E	Q	N
D	C	U	O	C	R	W	C	J	E	F	L	Z	U	L
S	H	Z	J	M	U	V	U	D	T	R	I	Y	D	F
R	P	G	S	V	B	F	T	C	A	J	S	V	C	G
W	Q	X	E	R	B	E	I	B	P	M	O	H	P	U
H	D	F	D	P	I	J	E	R	O	D	P	X	K	B
V	O	S	W	Q	N	X	F	W	D	R	O	B	V	A
F	P	E	Y	D	U	R	L	U	M	K	D	J	Z	J
B	M	V	N	M	J	N	Y	Z	Y	D	Z	W	D	R
X	I	C	A	T	E	R	P	I	E	F	J	I	H	A
L	W	R	D	K	P	M	J	H	C	W	V	C	Z	H
I	D	K	C	W	Y	Q	Y	M	R	V	D	U	X	C
T	R	B	U	F	T	L	O	V	A	K	I	V	J	S

WHO'S THAT POKÉMON?

DEWPIDER

MASTER OF DISGUISE

PAGE 32

Mimikyu is Jessie's partner.

ULTRA SCRAMBLE

PAGE 33

1 PHERAMOSA
2 GUZZLORD
3 NIHILEGO
4 BLACEPHALON
5 NAGADANEL
6 XURKITREE

The secret Ultra Beast is:
POIPOLE.

FREQUENT FLYERS

PAGE 34

A & E, B & F, C & H, D & I. The odd one out is G.
Cutiefly – it's not a Flying-type Pokémon.

FALSE FRIENDS

PAGE 35

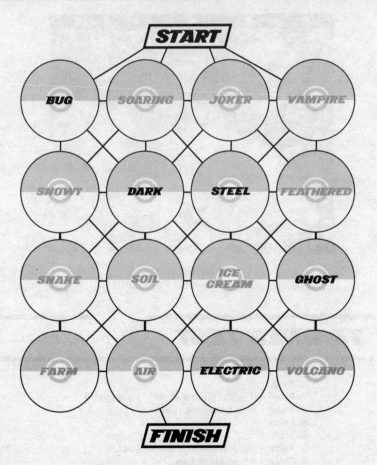

START

BUG	SOARING	JOKER	VAMPIRE
SNOWY	DARK	STEEL	FEATHERED
SNAKE	SOIL	ICE CREAM	GHOST
FARM	AIR	ELECTRIC	VOLCANO

FINISH

PUZZLING POKÉ BALLS

PAGE 36

1. D – Dusk Ball
2. C – Heal Ball
3. F – Nest Ball
4. E – Great Ball
5. A – Repeat Ball
6. B – Dive Ball

MIND BLOWN!

PAGE 37

ANOTHER NAME
1. The Fireworks Pokémon.

TRAINER TEST

PAGE 38

1. True.
2. False – it is the Guardian of Ula'ula Island.
3. False – he's a student there.
4. False.
5. True.
6. False – the Pokémon is Bounsweet.
7. False – it's an Ultra Ball.
8. True.

POISON PAL

The Pokémon is:
POIPOLE

PROBLEM PATTERNS

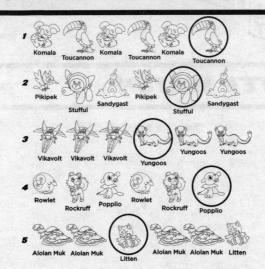

1 Komala, Toucannon, Komala, Toucannon, Komala, Toucannon

2 Pikipek, Stufful, Sandygast, Pikipek, Stufful, Sandygast

3 Vikavolt, Vikavolt, Vikavolt, Yungoos, Yungoos, Yungoos

4 Rowlet, Rockruff, Popplio, Rowlet, Rockruff, Popplio

5 Alolan Muk, Alolan Muk, Litten, Alolan Muk, Alolan Muk, Litten

There are 24 Luvdisc.

WEB WEAVING

PAGE 43

SPECIES SWITCH

PAGE 44

DARK
BARK
BANK
RANK
RACK
ROCK

Alolan Persian
Dark type. ☑

Lycanroc (Midday Form)
Rock type. ☑

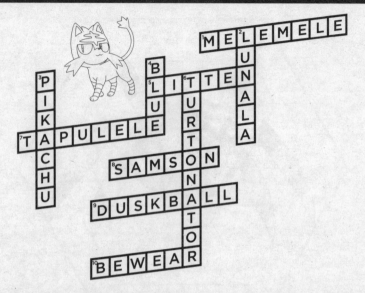

The crossword answers:

1. MELEMELE
2. LUNALA
3. PIKACHU
4. BLUE
5. LITTEN
6. BURTONATOR
7. TAPULELE
8. SAMSON
9. DUSKBALL
10. BEWEAR

PONI PUZZLE

PAGE 46

The coordinates are:
Pikachu   D3
Ash   C7
Ribombee   E5
Tapu Fini B1
Kommo-o   G4
Jangmo-o   B4

SLEEPY SIDEKICK

PAGE 47

Principal Oak's Pokémon pal is Komala.

RISKY ROUTE

PAGE 48

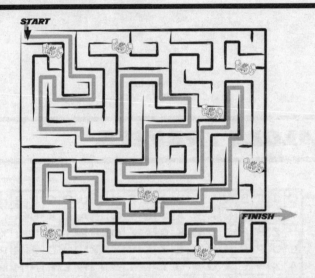

I CHOOSE YOU!

PAGE 49

A	B	C	D	E	F	G	H	I	J	K	L	M
1	2	3	4	5	6	7	8	9	10	11	12	13

N	O	P	Q	R	S	T	U	V	W	X	Y	Z
14	15	16	17	18	19	20	21	22	23	24	25	26

Kiawe chose to battle with TURTONATOR.

Necrozma:
Dawn Wings.

ALOLA TRAVELS

PAGE 51

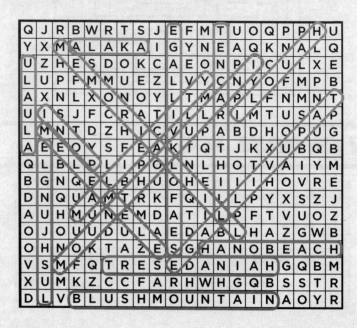

ON THE DOUBLE

PAGE 52

HATS OFF!

PAGE 53

KUKUI'S CODE

PAGE 54

The six-letter word is: ROWLET.
Other words include: TROWEL, LOWER, TOWEL, TOWER,
OWLET, WROTE, WELT, WORE, WORT, LORE, ROLE, ROTE,
TORE, LOW, OWL, OWE, TOE, TWO, WET, WOE, LET, LOT,
ORE, ROE, ROT, ROW, TOW, OW, WE, OR, TO.

SNACK TIME

PAGE 55

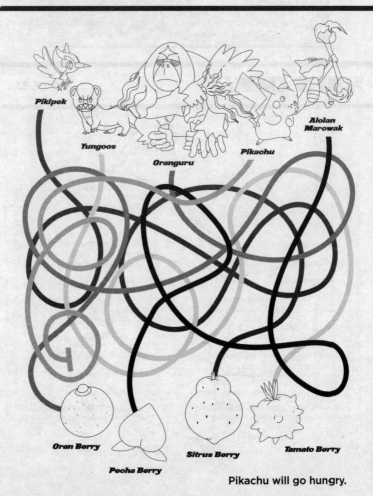

Pikipek

Yungoos

Oranguru

Pikachu

Alolan Marowak

Oran Berry

Pecha Berry

Sitrus Berry

Tamato Berry

Pikachu will go hungry.

ASH IMPOSTERS

PAGE 56

GUESS THE GUARDIAN
Tapu Koko gave Ash his Z-Ring.

ISLAND PATH

PAGE 57

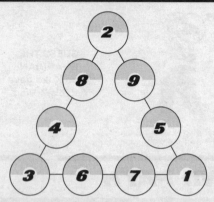

Note: the numbers 6 and 7 can be switched around.

CHINOSITI

S H I I N O T I C

ATOMFINS

F O M A N T I S

CUDEYEDIE

D E C I D U E Y E

ERLWOT

R O W L E T

BENOWTSUE

B O U N S W E E T

EARNATSE

T S A R E E N A

MULEROLL

M O R E L U L L

The secret Grass-type Pokémon is: STEENEE.

Rockruff — Lycanroc (Midday Form)
Alolan Meowth — Alolan Persian
Stufful — Bewear
Alolan Vulpix — Alolan Ninetales
Sandygast — Palossand

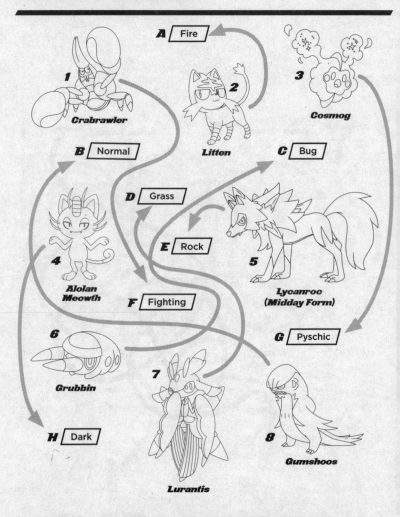

A Fire

1 Crabrawler

2 Litten

3 Cosmog

B Normal

C Bug

D Grass

4 Alolan Meowth

E Rock

5 Lycanroc (Midday Form)

F Fighting

G Pyschic

6 Grubbin

7

H Dark

8 Gumshoos

Lurantis

SCREEN SCRAMBLE

PAGE 62

Burnet's message reads:
AN ULTRA WORMHOLE HAS BEEN
DETECTED OFF THE COAST OF
MELEMELE ISLAND.

Komala 5

Charjabug 4

Mudbray 5

Litten 4

Turtonator 1

Drampa 3

Bewear 4

Cutiefly 8

Alolan Raichu 5

D	I	N	A	U	Q	A	R	A	P	L	O	I	B	Z
N	R	V	B	L	Q	N	I	R	V	I	V	X	N	L
W	Z	E	A	R	U	W	I	W	L	B	X	F	D	P
I	I	Y	D	C	I	M	J	P	I	J	S	B	B	E
V	Q	S	X	I	A	O	P	D	S	P	U	E	K	X
O	A	Q	H	R	P	O	N	D	J	Y	M	I	T	N
E	Z	O	I	I	P	W	J	N	A	U	W	N	C	O
N	J	N	Q	V	W	C	E	T	E	K	P	I	Z	X
Q	A	B	J	O	S	A	D	D	P	U	P	F	N	C
S	O	U	Z	I	F	P	S	M	E	M	X	U	F	W
A	W	I	V	Z	X	L	T	H	L	U	A	P	U	I
M	W	P	U	E	H	K	M	V	I	K	M	A	V	M
O	A	T	U	O	P	P	P	E	R	U	W	T	P	P
D	K	B	A	B	G	X	N	R	H	F	M	I	X	O
Y	Y	B	R	U	X	I	S	H	O	R	L	K	G	D